CW00384786

# Immune-Boosting Cookbook

## Supporting your Immune System through Diet

### Cooking for Health 2

By

**Minna Rose**

LionheART Publishing House
Harrogate
UK

lionheartpublishinghouse@gmail.com

First published in Great Britain in 2019 by
LionheART Publishing House

Copyright © Minna Rose 2019
ISBN: 978-1-910115-87-9

This book is copyright under the Berne Convention
No reproduction without permission
All rights reserved.

# Contents

# Introduction to the Immune-Boosting Cookbook

The immune system is your body's defence system against bacteria, viruses, parasites and fungi, and a number of organs are involved in this, mainly in the production of the lymphocyte cells that neutralise or destroy the invading micro-organisms.

The most important of these organs are the spleen, bone marrow and blood vessels, as well as lymph nodes (glands) plus the lymphatic vessels which transport the lymphocytes to the blood stream.

A number of factors can impact the effectiveness of your immune system, such as stress, smoking and over-indulging in alcohol, and minimising those three things can help increase your body's strength. Eating a healthy diet, packed with nutrients, is another positive step you can take, and the recipes in this book are designed to include the main vitamins and minerals to boost your immune system, such as vitamins A, C, D and E, plus folate, iron, selenium and zinc.

Eating healthily does not mean giving up the tastes you enjoy, and whilst you can go to extremes and eat only fresh, raw superfoods, that may present difficulties at the family dinner table. The meals may be super-healthy, but the stress involved in trying to persuade the kids (or even your other half) to eat it may well negate those benefits!

In the *Immune-Boosting Cookbook*, Minna Rose has taken family favourites and added a healthy twist; for example, chicken Kievs – skinless chicken fillets, homemade fresh garlic and parsley butter, all in a crunchy oat coating with sweet potato fries and a colourful salsa – great ingredients to make a delicious and nutritious family dinner.

With a little lateral thinking, puddings and desserts can be healthy too. Using natural Greek yoghurt, berries, citrus, apples and oats, many delicious healthy desserts are possible – even the occasional cheesecake!

Having lived with a chronic pain condition for over 25 years, Minna Rose has spent a great deal of time researching ways in which she can help her own health. After noticing that a flare-up followed every cough or cold, she focused on the immune system and building its strength through her diet, and has shared the tastiest of these recipes in this *Immune-Boosting Cookbook*.

If you suffer from any health issues, including an immune-system disorder, please consult your doctor about your diet and management strategies.

References:
www.telegraph.co.uk
https://www.healthline.com/
https://www.stanfordchildrens.org/
https://health.clevelandclinic.org

# Immune-Boosting Cookbook

# 1. Chicken & Vegetable Soup

This is ideally made the day after a roast chicken dinner so you can make your own stock using the chicken carcass for extra nutrients.

Serves 4

### Ingredients

1 litre/2 pints/4 cups chicken stock
(homemade if possible
using a chicken carcass plus a
roughly chopped peeled onion,
leek, carrot, bay leaf, salt and 6
black peppercorns)
500g/1 lb chicken meat
– cut into bite-sized pieces
1 onion – peeled and diced
1 leek – washed and sliced
6 carrots – washed and chopped
2 parsnips – washed and chopped
3 sticks celery – washed and chopped
100g/4 oz/½ cup pearl barley
2 cloves garlic – peeled and minced
50g/2 oz/¼ cup fresh sage – chopped (plus extra for garnish)
Freshly ground black pepper
Olive oil for frying

### Preparation

1. Make the stock (this can be done the day before), by placing the chicken carcass (either whole or in pieces) and other stock ingredients into a large pan. Cover with hot water, bring to the boil, then turn the heat to low. Cover and simmer for 1 hour. Once cooled, strain the liquid into a large jug ready for the soup.

2. Add a tablespoon of olive oil in the bottom of a large, heavy based pot, and place on a medium heat. Add the diced onion and gently fry until soft.

3. Add the chicken and stir fry until the chicken has browned. Add the garlic and chopped veg and stir well.

4. Add the stock and the pearl barley, bring to the boil then reduce the heat to a low simmer. Add the chopped sage and freshly ground black pepper and simmer for 30–45 minutes until the vegetables are soft, and the pearl barley is tender.

5. Taste, adjust the seasoning if necessary, and serve sprinkled with a little fresh sage, along with fresh, crusty white bread and butter.

## 2. Carrot & Coriander Soup

This is ideally made the day after a roast chicken dinner so you can make your own stock using the chicken carcass for extra nutrients.

A stick or soup blender is helpful for this recipe.

Serves 4

### Ingredients

1 litre/2 pints/4 cups chicken stock (homemade if possible using a chicken carcass plus a roughly chopped peeled onion, leek, carrot, bay leaf, salt and 6 black peppercorns)
2 onions – peeled and diced
1kg/2 lb carrots – washed and chopped
Juice of 2 oranges (or 100ml/½ cup fresh orange juice)
50g/2oz/¼ cup fresh coriander (cilantro) – chopped
Salt and freshly ground black pepper
Sunflower oil for frying

### Preparation

1. Make the stock (this can be done the day before), by placing the chicken carcass (either whole or in pieces) and other stock ingredients into a large pan. Cover with hot water, bring to the boil, then turn the heat to low. Cover and simmer for 1 hour. Once cooled, strain the liquid into a large jug ready for the soup.

2. Gently fry the onion in a large stock pot with 1 tablespoon of sunflower oil until soft.

3. Add the carrots and stock (to just cover the carrots), then the orange juice, salt and pepper. Bring to the boil, then simmer for approx. 30 minutes or until the carrots are soft.

4. Add the coriander and use a soup stick or blender to blitz. Taste and adjust the seasoning if necessary.

5. Serve, sprinkled with a little more chopped coriander and grated carrot, with warm bread and butter.

# 3. Spiced Butternut Squash Soup
A stick or soup blender is helpful for this recipe
Serves 4

## Ingredients

1 litre/2 pints/ 4 cups chicken stock (homemade if possible with a chicken carcass plus a roughly chopped peeled onion, leek, carrot, bay leaf, salt and 6 black peppercorns)

1 butternut squash – peeled, deseeded and roughly chopped.

2 onions – peeled and diced

2 carrots – washed and chopped

1 x 400g tin (1½ cups) chopped tomatoes

150ml/½ cup soured cream

1"/2cm piece fresh ginger – peeled and chopped

3 cloves garlic – peeled and minced

1 teaspoon ground cumin

1 teaspoon ground coriander

1 teaspoon turmeric

¼ teaspoon cayenne pepper

Salt and black pepper

Sunflower oil for frying

## Preparation

1. Make the stock (this can be done the day before), by placing the chicken carcass (either whole or in pieces) and other stock ingredients into a large pan. Cover with hot water, bring to the boil, then turn the heat to low. Cover and simmer for 1 hour. Once cooled, strain the liquid into a large jug ready for the soup.

2. Gently fry the onion and garlic in a large stock pot with 1 tablespoon of sunflower oil until soft.

3. Add the butternut squash, carrots, tomatoes and stock (to just cover the vegetables). Add the ginger, cumin, coriander seed, turmeric, cayenne pepper, salt and black pepper and stir well.

4. Bring to the boil, then simmer for approx. 30 minutes or until the squash and carrots are soft.

4. Add the soured cream, and use a soup stick or blender to blitz. Taste and adjust the seasoning if necessary.

5. Serve, sprinkled with a little fresh red chilli and a swirl of soured cream, with warm bread and butter.

## 4. Immune-Boosting Salad

I've suggested a selection of ingredients, but the key thing here is to include as many fresh foods as possible, and the more colourful your salad the better! Why not try adding avocado and green beans, mango and apple, even orange segments and strawberries?

### **Ingredients**
Baby spinach
Radicchio
Red & yellow pepper
Spring onions
Cherry tomatoes
Sweetcorn
Carrot – washed and grated
or spiralized
Beetroot – peeled and grated
Red chilli – deseeded and
chopped if you like a bit of
heat

### For the French Dressing
1 shallot
1 garlic clove
1 teaspoon Dijon mustard
2 teaspoons honey
1 teaspoon fresh herbs – rosemary, sage and thyme
Salt and pepper
2 tablespoons white wine vinegar
4 tablespoons extra virgin olive oil

### **Preparation**

#### For the salad
Wash, thoroughly drain, then chop the salad ingredients
Place in a salad bowl and toss to mix well

#### For the French Dressing
1. Peel and finely dice the shallot and garlic clove and mix in a jar with the mustard, honey, herbs, salt and pepper.

2. Add the vinegar and oil and shake well before serving.

# 5. Red Cabbage Slaw

## Ingredients

½ red cabbage
6 carrots
150g/½ cup sultanas
2 tablespoons mayonnaise

## Preparation

1. Shred the red cabbage as finely as possible, discarding the tough stalks.

2. Peel and grate the carrots.

3. Mix the vegetables in a bowl then add the sultanas and mayonnaise.

4. Stir well.

# 6. A Pair of Salsas

## Tomato Salsa Ingredients

4 fresh tomatoes
1 red pepper
1 red onion
Juice of 1 lemon
25g/1 oz fresh coriander leaves (cilantro)

## Preparation

1. Chop the tomatoes, peel and dice the onion, and deseed and dice the red pepper.

2. Mix them together in a bowl.

3. Squeeze in the lemon juice.

4. Chop the coriander leaves and add to the salsa.

5. Mix well and transfer to a serving bowl.

## Pineapple & Mint Salsa Ingredients

1 x 500g can (1 ½ cups) pineapple pieces
6 spring onions
1 red chilli
1 lemon
25g/1 oz fresh mint leaves

## Preparation

1. Drain the can of pineapple and put the pieces into a bowl. (If you have rings rather than pieces, cube them first)

2. Slice the spring onions and add to the pineapple.

3. Dice the red chilli (deseed first if you would rather have less heat) and add.

4. Squeeze the juice of the lemon over the ingredients so far.

5. Chop the mint, add and mix well.

6. Transfer to a serving bowl.

# 7. German Omelette

Speck and prosciutto contain high amounts of fat and sodium so should not be eaten often, but they also contain iron and zinc, both of which help the immune system, so I do like to indulge, although only occasionally.

Serves 2

## Ingredients

4 eggs
2 tablespoons plain flour
150g/4-6 oz Speck (can be substituted with prosciutto or good quality, dry-cured bacon)
1 tablespoon fresh marjoram
1 tablespoon fresh parsley
Salt and pepper
100g /4 oz Gruyere cheese
15g/½ oz butter for frying

## Method

1. Break the eggs into a bowl and add the flour.

2. Dice the Speck and add to the bowl.

3. Finely chop the fresh herbs and add.

4. Grind in salt and pepper and whisk the mixture well.

5. Grate the cheese into a separate bowl and put to one side.

6. Melt the butter in a frying pan then pour in the egg mixture.

7. Cook for 1-2 minutes, until the base is golden brown (use a fish slice to check).

8. Flip the omelette with a large spatula or fish slice, sprinkle the cheese over the top, cover with a lid or plate and switch off the heat to allow the residual heat to finish the cooking.

9. Serve with salad and potatoes.

**Tip:** Any remaining mixture can be kept in a jar in the fridge and cooked as above within a few days – just give the jar a good shake first.

# 8. German Herring Salad

## Ingredients

4 salted herring fillets
1 red onion
1 apple
2-4 dill gherkins
(depending on size)
4 tablespoons thick natural
Greek yoghurt
2-3 tablespoons white wine
vinegar
1 teaspoon Dijon mustard
Freshly ground black pepper
Fresh chives

## Method

1. Soak the herring fillets for 1-2 hours, then drain well. Cut into 2cm/1" pieces.

2. Peel and thinly slice the onion and roughly chop the apples and gherkins.

3. Mix the herring, onion, apple, gherkin, mustard, vinegar and plenty of black pepper together.

4. Add the yoghurt and mix well so that everything is coated, then transfer to your serving dish.

5. Chop the chives and sprinkle over as garnish.

6. Serve with rye bread or pumpernickel.

**Tip**: If you can't get salted herrings, you can use prepared rollmop herring, then omit the vinegar as they are already pickled.

# 9. Tuna Fishcakes
## Serves 2-4

### Ingredients

2 x 120g/4 oz cans tuna in spring
    water – drained
2 large potatoes – cooked and
    mashed
1 egg – beaten
3-4 spring onions – thinly sliced
1 red chilli – deseeded and
    chopped
25g/1 oz fresh parsley – chopped
Juice of 1 lemon
Black pepper– freshly ground

100g/½ cup plain flour
A second egg – beaten
100g/½ cup breadcrumbs
1-2 lemons – sliced into wedges to serve

For the Dip
200g /1 cup natural Greek yoghurt
1 clove garlic – peeled and minced
Juice of 1 lemon
25g/1 oz fresh herb – chopped: parsley,
    chives, dill or coriander all work well

### Preparation

1. Roughly break up the fish in a bowl, then add the mashed potato, 1 beaten egg, the spring onion, parsley, lemon juice and black pepper.

2. Mix well and form into patties.

3. Coat the fishcakes with flour, dip into the second beaten egg, then coat with breadcrumbs and fry until golden.

4. Meanwhile, mix the dip ingredients together, and place in a small serving bowl.

5. Serve the fishcakes with a salad, a wedge of fresh lemon, and a side of warmed crusty white bread.

## 10. Tuna with Thai Butter

Flavoured butter is a wonderful way to add extra taste to dishes, and this Thai butter also works well with chicken and beef steak. What you don't use at the time of making, you can freeze, either in portions or in a roll to be sliced at the time of use.

### **Ingredients**

1 tuna steak per person
250g / ½ lb butter
4 stalks lemongrass
4-6 fresh red chillies
2 bulbs garlic
1 tablespoon Thai fish sauce

## **Preparation**

<u>First make the flavoured butter – this can be made ahead of time and refrigerated until you're ready to use it.</u>

1. Place the garlic bulbs (skin still on) in a small roasting dish and roast for 30 minutes at a high heat (240°C/450°F/gas mark 8).
2. Soften your butter in a bowl over a pan of simmering water, taking care not to melt.
3. Wash and chop the chillies and add to the butter. (If mixing by hand ensure they are chopped very finely.)
4. Peel the lemongrass stalks, cut away and discard the bulb and beat the stalks with a rolling pin to crush the fibres. Chop (very finely if mixing by hand) and add to the butter mixture. Add the fish sauce.
5. When the garlic is ready, remove it from the oven and place it on a chopping board to cool. Remove the cloves, then use the flat of a broad knife to squash the flesh of the garlic out of the skins. Add to the bowl.
6. Use a soup stick or food processor to blend the mixture, or beat with a wooden spoon to mix well.
7. Place into your desired cloche or moulds, or roll into a sausage shape in cling film to slice later, depending on how you wish to serve your butter. Refrigerate to harden.

<u>For the Tuna:</u>
1. Take the butter out of the fridge to allow it to soften slightly at room temperature.
2. Rinse the tuna steaks under cold water, then pat dry with a paper towel.
2. The tuna will not take long to cook, so prepare your accompaniments in good time (serving suggestions: noodles and a stir fry, or salad and jacket potato).
3. Melt one small slice of the Thai butter per steak in a heavy-based frying pan.
4. As soon as this starts sizzling, add the tuna steaks to the pan.
5. Cook for 2-3 minutes, then turn (only turn the fish once).
6. After 2 minutes, use a fork to test the edge of the fish, and remove from the heat as soon as it starts to flake.
7. Serve immediately, topped with a fresh slice of butter, together with noodles and a stir fry, or salad and jacket potato.

# 11. Mussels in a Garlic, Parsley and White Wine Sauce

Serves 2

## Ingredients

1 kg/2lb mussels –
scrubbed and debearded
1 onion – peeled
3 garlic cloves - peeled
150ml/⅔ cup dry white
wine
300ml/1¼ cups soured
cream
25g/1 oz fresh parsley

## Preparation

1. Carefully check the mussels and discard any that are open.

2. Finely dice the onion and crush the garlic, and fry both until the onion is soft.

3. Add the wine and bubble until the alcohol has evaporated (the smell will become less pungent).

4. Take off the heat and stir in the soured cream.

5. Return to the heat, let the sauce bubble and add the mussels. Turn the heat down to a gentle simmer, cover and cook for approx. 4 minutes until all the mussels are open. (Discard any that remain closed.)

6. Chop the parsley and add the majority to the pan, saving a small amount to sprinkle over the final plate.

7. Serve with warm, crusty buttered bread.

# 12. Spaghetti with King Prawns
Serves 4

## Ingredients

400 g/1 lb fresh spaghetti (or 300g/10 oz dried)
1 tablespoon olive oil
1 red onion – peeled and diced
2 cloves garlic – peeled and crushed or minced
2 red chillies – finely sliced (deseeded if you prefer less heat)
1 x 400g tin (1½ cups) chopped tomatoes
Salt and freshly ground black pepper
1 teaspoon golden caster sugar
250g/10 oz king prawns – raw and shelled
150g/5 oz fresh, baby leaf spinach
Flat leaf parsley and fresh, grated parmesan for garnish

## Preparation

1. Heat the oil in a large, heavy-based saucepan, then add the onion and fry gently until soft.

2. Add the garlic and chillies and fry, stirring for another minute.

3. Add the chopped tomatoes and sugar, and stir as you bring to a boil, then reduce the heat. Season with salt and freshly ground black pepper and simmer for 10 minutes, stirring occasionally.

4. Add the king prawns and cook, stirring, for approx. 4-5 minutes, until they turn pink.

5. Meanwhile cook the spaghetti in hot water until it is al dente – 2 minutes if using fresh, 4 minutes if using dried.

6. Add the spaghetti and spinach to the main pan, and cook for a further 1-2 minutes until the spinach has wilted.

7. Serve with a garnish of flat leaf parsley and freshly grated parmesan cheese.

# 13. Lemon and Coriander Fish

## Ingredients

White fish steaks or fillets – 1 per person
1 lemon
1 garlic clove
1 teaspoon paprika
1 teaspoon ground coriander seed
Salt and pepper
1 tbsp sunflower oil
1 red onion – peeled and diced
1 red chilli – diced
25g/1 oz fresh coriander (cilantro)

## Preparation

1. Juice the lemon and mix this with the peeled, crushed garlic clove, paprika, ground coriander, salt and pepper.

2. Rub this mix into the flesh of fish, then leave to marinate for half an hour.

3. Heat the sunflower oil in a large frying pan. Add the fish (skin side down if using fillets).

4. Pour any remaining marinade into the pan, add the sliced red onion and deseeded, chopped red chilli.

5. Turn the fish when it's cooked halfway through, and turn the heat off.

6. Add a handful of chopped fresh coriander.

7. Cover and allow residual heat to cook through the rest of the fish.

8. Serve with fries or mashed potatoes and an immune-boosting salad.

# 14. Salmon with Honey and Lime

Serves 2

## Ingredients

2 salmon fillets
30g/1 oz butter
1 clove garlic, peeled
Juice of 1 lime
Juice of ½ lemon
100ml/½ cup white wine
1-2 teaspoons runny honey
25g/1 oz/ 2 tablespoons fresh coriander leaves (cilantro)

Serve with noodles and a spinach salad

## Preparation

1. Melt the butter in a frying pan. Add the crushed/minced garlic and fry for 1 minute.

2. Add the salmon fillets, skin side down.

3. Add the juice of the lime and half lemon, wine and honey. Stir around the salmon.

4. Simmer for 3-5 minutes, stirring occasionally, until the salmon is cooked through most of its thickness.

5. Turn the salmon, sprinkle in the chopped coriander/cilantro, and turn off the heat.

6. Leave in the pan for 2 minutes for the residual heat to finish cooking the fish.

7. Meanwhile, cook the noodles according to the instructions on the packet and serve with a spinach salad.

# 15. Salmon and Broccoli Penne
Serves 4

## Ingredients
400 g/1 lb fresh penne (or 300g/10 oz dried)
1 tablespoon olive oil
1 red onion – peeled and diced
2 cloves garlic – peeled and crushed or minced
1 red chilli – deseeded and thinly sliced
1 x 400g tin (1½ cups) chopped tomatoes
250g/10 oz tenderstem broccoli
Salt and freshly ground black pepper
150g/5 oz oak-smoked salmon – roughly chopped
(you can use cooked salmon steak or fillet instead if you prefer)
50g/2oz/¼ cup fresh basil – finely chopped (plus extra for garnish)
Fresh grated parmesan for garnish

## Preparation

1. Heat the oil in a large, heavy-based stock pot, then add the onion and fry gently until soft.

2. Add the garlic and chilli, and fry, stirring for another minute.

3. Add the chopped tomatoes and stir as you bring to a boil, then reduce the heat.

4. Slice the larger stems of the broccoli (or larger florets if using normal broccoli), then add to the sauce, season with salt and freshly ground black pepper and simmer for 10 minutes, stirring occasionally.

6. Meanwhile cook the penne in hot water until it is al dente – 2 minutes if using fresh, 4 minutes if using dried.

7. Add the salmon to the sauce and cook, stirring, on a low heat for 2 minutes.

8. Add the cooked penne and basil and cook for a further 1-2 minutes.

9. Serve with a garnish of basil leaves and parmesan if desired.

# 16. Honey Chilli Chicken
## Serves 2

### Ingredients

450g/1 lb chicken goujons
(mini breast fillets)
100g/½ cup plain flour
2 tablespoons sunflower oil
1"/2cm ginger – peeled and
grated
2 tablespoons runny honey
2 teaspoons cornflour
75 ml/⅓ cup cold water
1 tablespoon Chinese sweet
chilli sauce
Juice of 2 lemons
2 teaspoons soy sauce
1 red onion – peeled and sliced

### Preparation

1. Coat the chicken pieces in flour then fry in the sunflower oil until they turn golden brown.

2. Reduce the heat and cook the chicken through, then remove from the pan and drain, discarding most of the oil.

3. Add the grated ginger to the pan and fry over a low heat for 1 minute, then add the honey and stir for a further minute.

4. Mix the cornflour with the water then add to the pan with the chilli sauce, lemon juice and soy sauce. Bring to the boil, then reduce the heat to simmer until it thickens.

5. Add the chicken pieces and cook until they are heated through.

6. Add the onion slices and cook until they are soft.

7. Serve with rice or noodles and steamed pak choi or stir-fried vegetables.

# 17. Spanish Paella
Serves 4

This is a delicious way to eat a great deal of goodness.

I've been a little naughty in adding chorizo for that authentic Spanish flavour – this is fine occasionally, although not every week!

## **Ingredients**

1 tablespoon olive oil

4 chicken thighs – filleted and cut into bite-sized pieces

1 x 400g tin (1½ cups) chopped tomatoes

50g/2oz/¼ cup chorizo – cut into small nuggets

1 red onion – peeled and diced

2 cloves garlic – peeled and crushed or minced

1 red pepper – deseeded and finely chopped

2 teaspoons smoked paprika

2 teaspoons turmeric

100g frozen peas

250g/8 oz/1 cup king prawns – peeled and cooked

50g/2 oz/¼ cup fresh parsley – finely chopped

200g/7 oz/¾ cup paella rice

Splash white wine

600ml/2½ cups hot water

Juice of ½ a lemon, plus lemon wedges for garnish

## **Preparation**

1. Heat the oil in a large heavy-based frying pan or stockpot. Add the chicken pieces and fry, stirring well, until they are golden.

2. Add the onion, garlic, pepper and chorizo, plus the turmeric and paprika. Stir well to coat, then add the chopped tomatoes. Mix well and fry for another 2 minutes.

3. Boil 500ml water to have it ready. Add the rice and splash of white wine to the pan, then mix well before adding the water.

4. Mix well and bring to the boil, then reduce the heat to medium and simmer for 15-20 minutes, stirring occasionally, until almost all the liquid is absorbed. Add a little more water if it starts to look a little dry – but don't worry about a few crispy bits, they're very tasty!

5. Add the prawns, peas and parsley, and mix well. Simmer for a further 5 minutes.

6. Squeeze the lemon juice over the paella, add an extra sprinkling of chopped fresh parsley, and serve with extra lemon wedges.

# 18. Chicken Curry

Curry is not always seen as a healthy option, but it is packed full of immune-boosting nutrients, as well as the wonder spice turmeric. Just use olive oil instead of ghee, and no more than you need, then it is a fabulous, healthy meal.

Serves 6-8

## **Ingredients**

1 kg/2 lb chicken breast – cubed (turkey breast also works well)

2 onions – peeled and sliced

2 garlic cloves – peeled and minced/crushed

1 red pepper – deseeded and chopped

4 chillies – sliced (makes a medium-hot curry –
this can be adjusted to your own heat preference)

2 beef stock cubes

2 teaspoons turmeric

1 teaspoon cumin

1 teaspoon ground coriander

200g/1 cup tomato puree

1 x 400g tin (1½ cups) chopped tomatoes

500g/2 cups natural yoghurt

1 teaspoon garam masala

50g/2oz/¼ cup chopped fresh coriander leaf (cilantro)

1 teaspoon cornflour

2 tablespoons olive oil

For a quick and easy raita to accompany your curry, mix 1-2 teaspoons of mint sauce with 200g (1 cup) of Greek natural yoghurt.

## **Preparation**

1. Fry the onion with the olive oil in a large pot until soft.

2. Add the garlic, chilli and red pepper and stir well.

3. Add the dried spices and crumbled stock cubes. Stir well.

4. Add the meat. Stir until browned – make sure to keep scraping the bottom of the pan to keep all that flavour.

5. Add the tomato puree. Stir.

6. Add the chopped tomatoes. Stir, then lower the heat and simmer very gently for 1½ hours, stirring occasionally to allow the meat to tenderise and the spices to mellow.

7. Add the yoghurt and garam masala and stir well.

8. Simmer for a further 30 minutes.

9. Mix the cornflour in a little cold water and add to the sauce to thicken if needed. Stir well and bubble through.

10. Add the chopped coriander.

11. Serve with rice or naan bread and raita.

# 19. Jerk Chicken with Jamaican Rice and Peas

One of my favourite meals – plenty of flavour, and with quite a kick.
Even better, you can decide how much of a kick you deliver – use red chillies or scotch bonnet, and enjoy!
(If it's too hot for some of your family and/or guests, then a dollop of crème fraiche will cool things down.)

You will need a food processor or stick blender for this recipe.
Serves 2

## Ingredients

4-6 chicken thigh fillets
2 limes – quartered into wedges

For the jerk marinade
6 spring onions – sliced
1 red pepper – deseeded and chopped
1-2 red chillies – or swap for Scotch bonnet if you like it really hot!
2 cloves garlic – peeled and chopped
1"/2cm fresh ginger – peeled and chopped
100g/½ cup tomato puree
100ml/½ cup dark rum
Juice of 1 lemon
2 tablespoons dark brown sugar
25g/1 oz fresh thyme leaves
1 teaspoon smoked paprika
1 teaspoon ground cumin
1 teaspoon ground allspice
1 teaspoon nutmeg
1 teaspoon cinnamon
Salt and freshly ground black pepper

For the Rice and Peas
1 tablespoon sunflower oil
100g/½ cup basmati rice
200ml/1 cup light coconut milk
2 chicken stock cubes
150ml/⅔ cup boiling water
200g tin (1 cup) black-eyed beans

## **Preparation**

1. Add all the marinade ingredients to a food processor and blitz to a paste.

2. Place the chicken thighs in a dish and add rub in the paste to marinade for at least 30 minutes, or overnight.

3. Switch on the oven to preheat: 200°C/400°F/gas mark 6

4. Place the marinated chicken pieces on a foil-lined oven tray, add the lime quarters and bake for 20 minutes.

5. Turn, spoon more marinade over them and bake for another 20 minutes.

6. Meanwhile, make the rice and peas by first heating the oil in a large non-stick saucepan.

7. Add the rice and coconut milk, and stir well.

8. In a separate jug, dissolve the stock cubes in the boiling water, mix well and add to the rice.

9. Bring to the boil, cover, then reduce the heat and simmer for 10 minutes.

10. Rinse the black-eyed beans, stir them into the rice, then remove from the heat and cover until all the liquid has been absorbed.

11. Check to see if the chicken juices are running clear, then serve. If not, turn the chicken pieces, baste with the marinade and bake for another 10-20 minutes until the chicken is fully cooked.

## 20. Provençale Chicken
Serves 4

### <u>Ingredients</u>

1-2 chicken pieces per person, depending on size
1 onion – peeled and diced
2 cloves garlic – peeled and crushed
12 tomatoes – roughly chopped
50g/2oz/¼ cup black olives – pitted
50g/2 oz/¼ cup tomato puree
25g/1 oz/2 tablespoons fresh thyme – chopped
25g/1 /2 tablespoons fresh marjoram – chopped
1 bay leaf
Salt and black pepper
Olive oil for frying

## **Preparation**

1. Switch on the oven to preheat to 200°C/400°F/gas mark 6.

2. Sprinkle the chicken pieces with olive oil, salt and pepper, place them on a lined baking tray, then put into the oven to cook for 15 minutes.

3. Heat the oil in a large pan and gently fry the onion until soft. Add the garlic and fry for a further 1-2 minutes.

4. Add the tomatoes, black olives, salt, pepper and herbs, then mix well.

5. Bring to the boil and simmer for 20 minutes to allow the flavours to develop and blend.

6. Meanwhile, turn the chicken pieces and replace them into the oven to cook for a further 10-15 minutes.

7. Mix the tomato puree into the sauce, then taste to check the seasoning. Simmer for a further 10 minutes.

8. Check the chicken to ensure the juices are running clear. If not, cook for a further 5 minutes and check again. When the juices are clear, remove the chicken from the oven, sprinkle with more chopped herbs, then cover with foil and leave to rest for 5 minutes.

9. Remove the bay leaf from the sauce, then serve poured over the chicken pieces with sweet potato mash or fries and salad.

This versatile sauce is also delicious with salmon or white fish fillets, or a succulent beef steak.

## 21. Crunchy Chicken Kievs
Serves 4

### **Ingredients**

4 large, skinned chicken breast fillets

100g/4 oz plain flour

2 eggs – beaten

150g/6 oz rolled oats

For the Garlic Butter

250g/½ lb butter

100g/4 oz fresh parsley

2 bulbs garlic

## **Preparation**

1. First make the garlic butter – this can be done ahead of time and the butter refrigerated or even frozen until it's time to use. Place the garlic bulbs (skin still on) in a small roasting dish and roast for 30 minutes at 200°C/400°F/gas mark 6.

2. Soften your butter in a bowl over simmering water, taking care not to melt it.

3. Wash and chop the parsley and add it to the butter. (If mixing by hand, ensure the herbs are chopped very finely.)

4. When the garlic is ready, remove it from the oven and put on a chopping board to cool. Remove the cloves, then use the flat of a broad knife to squash the flesh of the garlic out of the skins. Add to the bowl.

5. Use a soup stick or food processor to blend the mixture, or beat with a wooden spoon to mix well.

6. Place into your desired cloche or moulds, or roll it into a sausage shape in cling film to be sliced later. Refrigerate to harden for later use.

7. Switch on your oven to preheat to 200°C/400°F/gas mark 6.

8. Open out the skinned chicken breasts, and place a slice of the garlic butter into the fold (alternatively, slice the fleshiest part of the underside to create a pocket), then close the chicken over the butter to make a parcel.

9. Dip each breast into the flour, then the beaten egg, then coat thoroughly with the rolled oats.

10. Place on a greased/lined baking tray and cook in the oven for approx. 30 minutes.

11. It's inevitable that some of the butter will leak, so use this to baste the Kievs and cook for another 15-30 minutes until the oats are starting to brown and the chicken is cooked through (cut into one to check the juices are running clear if you are not sure). If no butter has leaked, well done! Just add a small knob of butter to the top of the Kievs.

12. Serve with a tomato and pepper salsa and sweet potato fries

(This would work well with a range of butters, for example a nice Béarnaise butter with tarragon, or sweet chilli butter – see Minna Rose's *Utterly Buttery Cookbook* for more ideas.)

## 22. Chilli con Carne

This is best made in bulk for big gatherings, or the remainder can be frozen for a quick and easy meal later. If you prefer to cook in smaller quantities, just halve all ingredients.

Serves 8

### Ingredients

1 tablespoon olive oil

2 onions – peeled and diced

4 garlic cloves – peeled and minced

3 red chillies – diced (deseed if you prefer a mild chilli)

2 carrots – peeled and chopped

1 kg/2 lb minced beef

4 rashers smoked bacon – chopped

2 red peppers – deseeded and chopped

2 teaspoons chilli powder (omit if you prefer a mild chilli)

1 teaspoon mustard powder

2 teaspoons Worcestershire sauce

2 beef stock cubes

2 x 400g tins (3 cups) red kidney beans – washed and drained

2 x 400g tin (3 cups) chopped tomatoes

200g/¾ cup tomato puree

1 tablespoon beef gravy granules

Cornflour to thicken if necessary

## **Preparation**

1. Fry the diced onion in the olive oil until soft.

2. Add the crushed/minced garlic cloves, sliced chillies, chopped carrots and chopped bacon. Stir 1 minute.

3. Add the minced beef and stir until browned.

4. Add the peppers and stir.

5. Add the chilli powder, mustard powder, Worcester sauce and crumbled stock cubes. Mix well.

6. Add the tomato puree, and stir in.

7. Add the kidney beans and chopped tomatoes. Stir.

8. Add the gravy granules. Stir.

9. Lower the heat and simmer, stirring occasionally for 1 hour.

10. Serve with rice, plus soured cream on the side if desired.

# 23. Meatballs in Tomato and Red Pepper Sauce with Pasta
Serves 4

## Ingredients

400 g/1 lb fresh pasta
(or 300g/10 oz dried)
Grated parmesan to
garnish

For the Meatballs
250g/8 oz minced beef
250g/8 oz minced
pork
1 bread roll
1 egg
Salt and pepper
50g/2oz/¼ cup plain
flour
Olive oil for frying

For the Sauce

1 tablespoon olive oil
1 onion – peeled and diced
2 cloves garlic – peeled and minced
1 red pepper – deseeded and sliced
2 x 400g tins (3 cups) chopped tomatoes
1 tablespoon tomato puree
Handful of cherry tomatoes for extra texture
1 teaspoon Worcestershire sauce
50ml/¼ cup red wine
1 teaspoon caster sugar
2 beef stock cubes
50g/2oz/¼ cup fresh Italian herbs – basil, oregano and thyme – chopped
Salt and pepper

# **Preparation**

Sauce

This can be prepared ahead of time, or prepared in bulk and frozen in batches for easy use at a later time.

1. Gently fry the diced onion in the oil until soft.
2. Add the garlic and sliced red peppers, and stir fry for 1 minute.
3. Add the tomato puree, and stir well.
4. Add the chopped tomatoes, cherry tomatoes, Worcestershire sauce, red wine, and caster sugar and stir well as you bring it to a simmer.
5. Crumble in the beef stock cubes, and mix well until they have dissolved.
6. Turn the heat down, add the majority of the chopped herbs (keeping some back for garnish), plus salt and pepper, and leave to simmer for half an hour, stirring occasionally.
7. Taste to check your seasoning, and add a touch more herbs, sugar, salt and/or pepper if required, stir in well, and leave to simmer a further 10 minutes, then turn off the heat and allow to cool.


Meatballs

You can buy them mixed, formed and ready to cook, but why not make your own?

1. Soak the bread in cold water, then squeeze it dry and chop.
2. Add all the ingredients except the flour into a bowl and mix well.
3. Form into balls, and roll in the flour.
4. Fry for 2-3 minutes, turning, to seal and brown, then put on one side.


Putting it all together

1. Add a dash of olive oil to a large saucepan and put on a medium heat.
2. When the oil is hot, add the meatballs, and give them a stir.
3. Spoon in enough tomato sauce for the number of diners.
4. Turn the heat down and cook on a low simmer for approx. 15 minutes, stirring occasionally.
5. Check the length of cooking time for your pasta – fresh cooks much quicker than dried – and add to a separate pan with hot water at the appropriate time. (The sauce can be kept on a low simmer for longer if your pasta is not ready in time.)
6. When the pasta is cooked (I usually do a taste test – careful of the hot water -to check), drain it through a sieve, then serve in large bowls with the meatballs and sauce, and add some grated parmesan and fresh herbs to garnish.

# 24. Seared Miso Steak with Rice and Pak Choi

Serves 4

## **Ingredients**
4 sirloin steaks
200g/1 cup jasmine rice
400ml/2 cups water
6 spring onions – finely sliced
2 chicken stock cubes
1 tablespoon sunflower oil

For the Miso Sauce
3 tablespoons miso paste (Japanese fermented soya beans)
2 tablespoons runny honey
2 tablespoons mirin (can be substituted with dry sherry)
1 teaspoon muscovado sugar
1 teaspoon dark soy sauce
2"/4cm piece root ginger – peeled and chopped
Juice of 1 lime

For the Pak Choi
200g/7oz tenderstem broccoli
200g/7oz pak choi
2 garlic cloves – peeled and minced or diced
1 red chilli – deseeded and finely sliced
1"/2cm piece root ginger – peeled and grated
1 tablespoon soy sauce
1 tablespoon sunflower oil

## **Preparation**

1. First make the miso sauce by adding all the ingredients to a saucepan over a low heat. Bring the sauce to a low simmer for 10 minutes, stirring regularly.

2. Boil the water in the kettle, while you heat the oil in a separate pan. Add the rice and spring onion to the oil and stir fry on a gentle heat.

3. Add the water and stir, then crumble in the stock cubes. Stir well until they dissolve.

4. Bring the rice mixture to the boil, then reduce the heat, cover and cook for 10 minutes, stirring occasionally to avoid sticking – once the 10 minutes has elapsed, switch the heat off, stir again and replace the cover to keep it warm until you are ready to serve.

5. When the miso sauce is ready, brush on to your steaks while you heat a griddle pan (or a frying pan with a tablespoon of sunflower oil).

6. Place the steaks – sauce-coated side down – in the pan, and brush more sauce on to the second side, then turn the steaks (only once). Check the steak is cooked to your preference by touch – rare: soft, medium: bouncy, well done: firm.

7. Meanwhile prepare the vegetables by first trimming the larger broccoli stems and separating the leaves of the pak choi. Heat the sunflower oil in a wok, then add the broccoli and a splash of water and stir fry for 2-3 minutes. Add the garlic, chilli and ginger and stir fry for 1 further minute. Add the pak choi leaves and the soy sauce, and stir fry another minute until the leaves wilt.

## 25 Chicken or Beef Fajita

This is a great family dinner – and everyone can put their own together according to their individual taste.

Serves 4

### Ingredients

1 tablespoon olive oil

1 onion – peeled and sliced

1 red and 1 green pepper – deseeded and sliced

2-4 red chillies – sliced (or 1-2 tablespoons chilli powder)

750g/1½ lb chicken breasts or sirloin steak – sliced into thin strips

1 teaspoon cumin

1 teaspoon paprika

1 teaspoon turmeric

1 teaspoon garlic granules

¼ teaspoon cayenne pepper

Serve With:

Tortilla wraps (1-3 per person depending on appetite)

Baby spinach leaves or lettuce

250 ml/1 cup soured cream

200g/7 oz cheddar cheese – grated

Tomato salsa (see earlier recipe)

### Preparation

1. Fry the onion in 1 tablespoon of olive oil until it turns golden, then turn the heat down to medium and add the pepper slices. Fry for 1-2 minutes.

2. Add the chicken or beef strips and stir fry until browned all over.

3. Turn the heat down to low and add the chillies, cumin, paprika, turmeric, garlic granules and cayenne pepper.

4. Stir fry until the meat is cooked through.

5. Either serve in a dish with the rest of the serving ingredients for people to help themselves, or build individual wraps starting by spreading soured cream on the tortilla, then add the spinach or lettuce, tomato salsa, the chicken and pepper mix and sprinkle with grated cheese before rolling.

# 26. Carrot Cake

## Ingredients

100g/4oz natural fruit sugar (available from most health food shops and some supermarkets)
125ml/½ cup sunflower oil (plus extra to grease the cake tins)
200g/7 oz wholemeal self-raising flour
2 teaspoons mixed spice (cinnamon, nutmeg & ginger)
1½ teaspoons bicarbonate of soda

2 eggs
Zest of 1 orange
175g/6 oz/¾ cup sultanas
200g/7 oz carrots – washed
and grated or finely chopped
by food processor

For the Topping
250g/9 oz cream cheese
25g/1 oz icing sugar
2 teaspoons vanilla extract
Mixed chopped nuts (optional)

## Preparation

1. Switch on the oven to preheat to 200°C/400°F/gas mark 6

2. Place the fruit sugar, eggs and sunflower oil into a bowl and beat well (2-3 minutes with an electric whisk, 10-15 minutes by hand).

3. Sift in the flour and bicarbonate of soda, and mix well.

4. Add the spice, orange zest, carrots and sultanas and mix well.

5. Grease two cake or loaf tins and fill with the cake mixture.

6. Bake for 40 minutes – this will leave the centre a little gooey which is delicious!

7. Allow to cool, then turn out of the tins on to a wire rack.

8. Mix the topping ingredients together, then liberally spread this over the cooled cakes before serving.

# 27. Apple Oat Crumble and Custard
Serves 4

## Ingredients
### For the Crumble
100g/4 oz plain flour
100g/4 oz Demerara sugar
75g/3 oz unsalted butter, plus extra for greasing
50g/2oz/¼ cup rolled oats

### For the Filling
450g/1 lb Bramley apples
50g/2oz/¼ cup golden caster sugar
1 tablespoon plain flour
½ teaspoon ground cinnamon

### For the Custard
2 large egg yolks
300ml/1 pint milk
1 tablespoon caster sugar
1 vanilla pod

## Preparation

1. Switch on the oven to preheat to 180°C/350°F/gas mark 4.

2. Sift the flour into a large bowl. Cube the butter and soften if needed in the microwave (taking care not to melt). Rub a few cubes at a time into the flour mixture until the mixture resembles breadcrumbs. Alternatively whizz together in a food processor.

3. Add the oats and sugar, and mix well.

4. Peel and core the apples, then slice the apples into large chunks. Place in a large bowl with the sugar, flour and sugar. Mix well, taking care not to bruise the apples.

5. Place the fruit into a greased ovenproof dish, and sprinkle the crumble mixture on top.

6. Bake 40-45 minutes until the crumble turns golden and the filling is bubbling.

7. To make the custard, first beat the egg yolks in a large bowl.

8. Heat the milk in a saucepan, along with the sugar and vanilla pod, until it is almost boiling.

9. Remove the vanilla pod and slowly pour the milk over the yolks, mixing well.

10. Return the mixture to the pan and cook until the custard thickens before serving.

# 28 New York Cheesecake

Containing calcium, zinc, vitamin A and vitamin B12, amongst other nutrients, a study in 2010 found that regularly eating cheese helps the immune system, especially as we grow older. The addition of oats in the biscuit base, lemon juice and eggs makes a New York cheesecake a healthier option than it first appears.

## Ingredients
125g/4 oz butter
200g/7 oz/1 cup oaty biscuits
(e.g. Hobnobs)
(alternatively mix 100g/3.5 oz/
½ cup digestive biscuits with
100g/½ cup rolled oats)
900g/4 cups cream cheese
150g/⅔ cup caster sugar
3 tablespoons plain flour
½ teaspoon vanilla extract
Juice of ½ lemon
3 large eggs (free range)
300ml/1¼ cups crème fraiche
Strawberries and
icing sugar to serve

## Preparation

1. Switch on the oven to preheat to 180°C/350°F/gas mark 4.

2. Melt the butter and crush the biscuits in a plastic bag using a rolling pin.

3. Mix the biscuits into the melted butter (plus the oats if using) and press into the base of a greased and lined cake tin.

4. Bake in the oven for 10 minutes, then set it aside to cool, leaving the oven switched on.

5. Mix the sugar and flour together in a food processor, add the cream cheese and beat well until smooth and creamy.

6. Add the eggs and beat in.

7. Add the crème fraiche a bit at a time, mixing well and using a rubber spatula to scrape the sides of the bowl clean to make sure everything is thoroughly mixed in.

8. Add the vanilla and lemon juice and beat in.

9. Add the mixture on top of the biscuit base and place the tin on a baking tray.

10. Bake in the oven for 45 minutes until the top is springy to a gentle touch.

11. Allow to cool, then transfer to the fridge to fully set.

12. Serve with strawberries and a sprinkling of icing sugar to garnish.

# 29. Yogurt, Honey and Berry Delice

A simple, fresh and healthy way to finish off a meal – using a local, raw honey is believed to be particularly beneficial for hay fever sufferers as it desensitises us to the local pollen, helping to reduce allergic reactions.

Serves 4

## Ingredients

400g/1½ cups natural Greek yoghurt

4 tablespoons local, raw runny honey

300g/10 oz/1½ cup fresh berries:
e.g: strawberries, raspberries and/or blueberries

Mixed chopped nuts to garnish – optional

## Preparation

1. Half-fill 4 serving glasses or bowls with 100g yoghurt (approx. 4 tablespoons) each.

2. Drizzle 1 tablespoon of honey over each yoghurt serving.

3. Add fresh berries to each dessert, and sprinkle with the nuts to serve.

# 30. Sticky Orange Flapjack

If you have a sweet tooth, this is a great way to satiate it.
By replacing the sugar and golden syrup with honey and agave syrup, you have all the sweetness you could want, yet the sugars are low GI, and you have plenty of goodness in the oats. The addition of orange and chocolate makes this even more decadent.

## Ingredients

425g/15oz rolled oats
250g/9oz unsalted butter
450g/1 lb jar/1 cup local runny honey
250ml/1 cup agave syrup (available from health food stores)
(If you can't find the agave syrup or similar, use 175g/6 oz/½ cup golden syrup)
50g/2oz/¼ cup chopped mixed nuts (optional)
3 tablespoons orange marmalade
1 tablespoon water
100g/3½ oz good quality dark chocolate

## Preparation

1. Switch on the oven to preheat to 200°C/400°F/gas mark 6.

2. Melt the butter over a very low heat, then pour it into a large mixing bowl with the honey and agave syrup.

3. Add the oats and mix well.

4. Turn the mixture into a greased baking tin, evenly spread, and sprinkle with the chopped nuts if you are using them.

5. Bake for 20-25 minutes until golden.

6. Melt the marmalade with the tablespoon of water, then spread over the flapjack.

7. Melt the chocolate in a bowl over a pan of hot water, ensuring the water does not touch the bowl, then drizzle or spread over the flapjack.

8. When cool, cut into slices to serve.

# The Minna Rose Cookbooks

## Cooking for Health

Low-Oxalate Cookbook: Osteoporosis, Fibromyalgia, Kidney Stones
Immune-Boosting Cookbook: Supporting your Immune System with Diet

## Cultural Tastes

German Cookbook
African Cookbook

## Utterly Buttery Cookbook:

Impress with flavoured butters for dinner parties, family suppers, barbecues,
and quick and easy meals

**If you would like to contact Minna or join Minna's mailing list to be kept updated of news, upcoming releases and special offers, you are very welcome at:
www.minnarose.com**

## A Message From Minna:

Thank you for purchasing this cookbook; I hope you enjoy these meals, and wish you good health.

If you have enjoyed any of these recipes, please do let me know by leaving a review on Amazon – I'd love to see which your favourites are!

Bon appetit,

*Minna Rose*

Printed in Great Britain
by Amazon

43837813R00028